the Weatherbirds

Ted Dewan

PUFFIN BOOKS

the Weatherbirds

Dedicated to Dr Edmond M. Dewan Ph.D.

His head perpetually in the stratosphere

PUFFIN BOOKS

Published by the Penguin Group
Penguin Books Ltd, 27 Wrights Lane, London W8 5TZ, England
Penguin Putnam Inc., 375 Hudson Street, New York, New York 10014, USA
Penguin Books Australia Ltd, Ringwood, Victoria, Australia
Penguin Books Canada Ltd, 10 Alcorn Avenue, Toronto, Ontario, Canada M4V 3B2
Penguin Books (NZ) Ltd, Private Bag 102902, NSMC, Auckland, New Zealand

Penguin Books Ltd, Registered Offices: Harmondsworth, Middlesex, England

On the World Wide Web at: www.penguin.com

First published by Viking 1999
Published in Puffin Books 2000
1 3 5 7 9 10 8 6 4 2

Copyright © Ted Dewan, 1999
All rights reserved

Design: Dave Allen
Weather Consultant: Barbara Taylor

The moral right of the author/illustrator has been asserted

Printed in Dubai

British Library Cataloguing in Publication Data
A CIP catalogue record for this book is available from the British Library

ISBN 0-140-38236-4

Contents

Professor Stork

Elmer

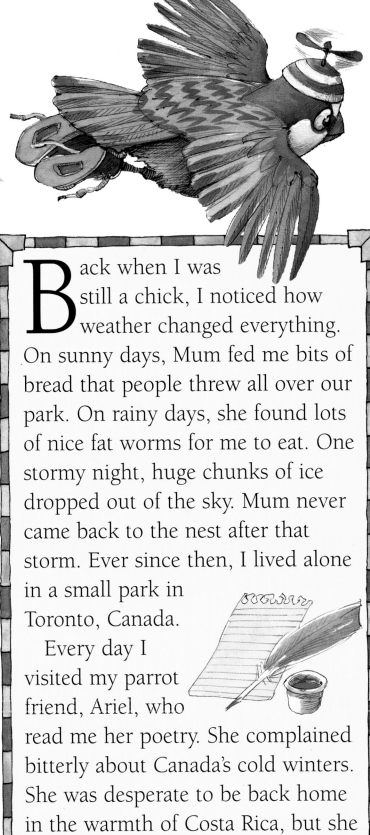

Back when I was still a chick, I noticed how weather changed everything. On sunny days, Mum fed me bits of bread that people threw all over our park. On rainy days, she found lots of nice fat worms for me to eat. One stormy night, huge chunks of ice dropped out of the sky. Mum never came back to the nest after that storm. Ever since then, I lived alone in a small park in Toronto, Canada.

Every day I visited my parrot friend, Ariel, who read me her poetry. She complained bitterly about Canada's cold winters. She was desperate to be back home in the warmth of Costa Rica, but she was stuck in a cage.

Until one chilly day in October, when the wind changed direction ...

Captain Goose

Ariel

The Beginning

'Ariel! Someone left your cage open!' I shouted. 'Now's your chance to fly out of there!'

'Oh, Sparrow,' said Ariel, 'I'd love to, but I'll freeze outside.'

'But you could fly back to Costa Rica,' I said. 'You said it's always hot there.'

'I can't,' she sighed. 'My wings are clipped – I can hardly fly. I'll be stuck here in Toronto for the rest of my life.'

'I know a very clever stork who might help you,' I said. 'Why don't we ask her if she can think of a way to bring you back home?' So Ariel gingerly left the cage. We fluttered out of the window and hopped over the rooftops to Professor Stork's workshop.

HOT 'N' COLD PLACES

Some places, like Costa Rica, are hot, while other places, like Canada, are warm in summer but cold in winter. This is because of the way the hot Sun's rays hit the curved surface of the Earth. The Sun's rays hit Costa Rica directly all year round. But Canada lies on a part of the Earth near the 'top' of the Earth, which is curved away from the Sun. Up there, the Sun's rays spread out over a wider area than they do in Costa Rica. This cuts down the heating power of the Sun, making Canada colder than Costa Rica.

The **North and South Poles** are the names of places on the 'top' and 'bottom' of the Earth. Midway between the North and South Poles is an imaginary circle around the Earth called the **equator.** The Sun hits the Earth's equator directly, so places near the equator, such as Costa Rica, stay hot all year round.

Warm air from the equator and cold air from the poles fight each other all the time. The air wars make the weather change constantly.

North Pole: Earth's 'top'

Toronto, Canada

equator

Costa Rica

South Pole: Earth's 'bottom'

Sun

WORLD WEATHER

Different places on the Earth have different weather. The personality of a place's weather is called its **climate**. A place's climate mainly depends on how close it is to the equator.

Temperate
warm and moist
(not too hot nor too cold)

Tropical Rainforest
hot and moist

Tropical Grasslands
with wet and dry hot seasons

4

Desert
hot and dry

Polar
cold and dry

SEE FOR YOURSELF
Spreading Sunlight

You will need: ✳ a torch ✳ a dark room or cupboard

1 Point the torch straight at the wall. Notice how bright the circle of light is. In this position, the torch light is like the sunlight shining on the Earth's equator with the sun directly overhead.

2 Now shine the torch on to the wall at an angle. The amount of light coming from the torch is the same, but the light is more spread out. It is also dimmer. Now the torch light is like the sunshine near the North and South Poles. The curved surface of the Earth makes sunlight spread near the poles in the same way that the torchlight spreads.

5

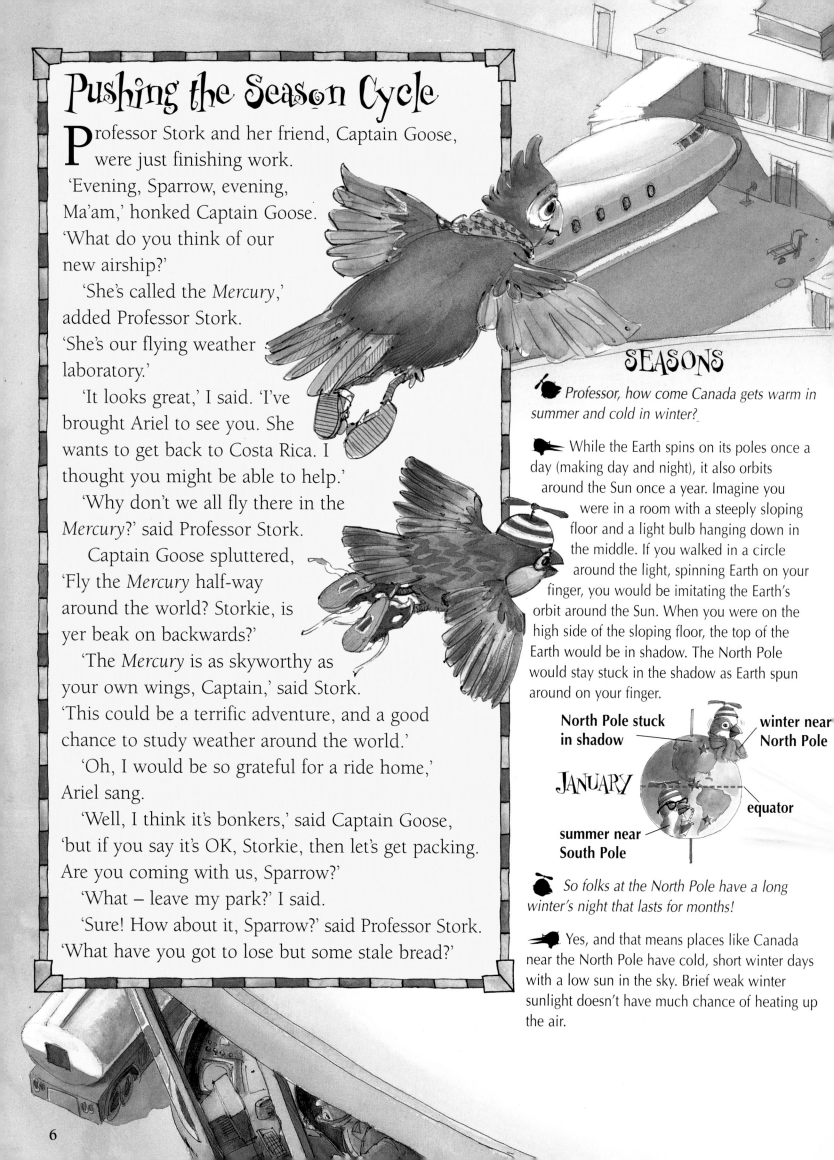

Pushing the Season Cycle

Professor Stork and her friend, Captain Goose, were just finishing work.

'Evening, Sparrow, evening, Ma'am,' honked Captain Goose. 'What do you think of our new airship?'

'She's called the *Mercury*,' added Professor Stork. 'She's our flying weather laboratory.'

'It looks great,' I said. 'I've brought Ariel to see you. She wants to get back to Costa Rica. I thought you might be able to help.'

'Why don't we all fly there in the *Mercury*?' said Professor Stork.

Captain Goose spluttered, 'Fly the *Mercury* half-way around the world? Storkie, is yer beak on backwards?'

'The *Mercury* is as skyworthy as your own wings, Captain,' said Stork. 'This could be a terrific adventure, and a good chance to study weather around the world.'

'Oh, I would be so grateful for a ride home,' Ariel sang.

'Well, I think it's bonkers,' said Captain Goose, 'but if you say it's OK, Storkie, then let's get packing. Are you coming with us, Sparrow?'

'What – leave my park?' I said.

'Sure! How about it, Sparrow?' said Professor Stork. 'What have you got to lose but some stale bread?'

SEASONS

Professor, how come Canada gets warm in summer and cold in winter?

While the Earth spins on its poles once a day (making day and night), it also orbits around the Sun once a year. Imagine you were in a room with a steeply sloping floor and a light bulb hanging down in the middle. If you walked in a circle around the light, spinning Earth on your finger, you would be imitating the Earth's orbit around the Sun. When you were on the high side of the sloping floor, the top of the Earth would be in shadow. The North Pole would stay stuck in the shadow as Earth spun around on your finger.

North Pole stuck in shadow

winter near North Pole

JANUARY

equator

summer near South Pole

So folks at the North Pole have a long winter's night that lasts for months!

Yes, and that means places like Canada near the North Pole have cold, short winter days with a low sun in the sky. Brief weak winter sunlight doesn't have much chance of heating up the air.

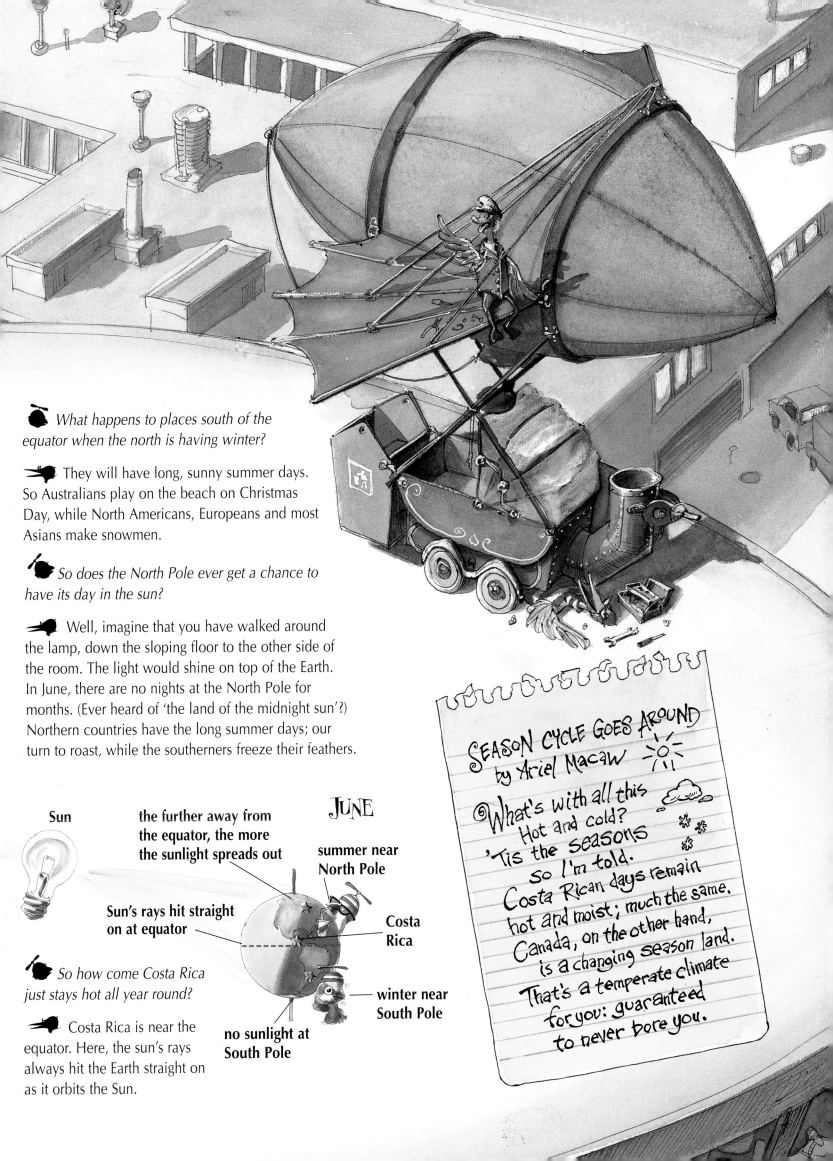

What happens to places south of the equator when the north is having winter?

They will have long, sunny summer days. So Australians play on the beach on Christmas Day, while North Americans, Europeans and most Asians make snowmen.

So does the North Pole ever get a chance to have its day in the sun?

Well, imagine that you have walked around the lamp, down the sloping floor to the other side of the room. The light would shine on top of the Earth. In June, there are no nights at the North Pole for months. (Ever heard of 'the land of the midnight sun'?) Northern countries have the long summer days; our turn to roast, while the southerners freeze their feathers.

Sun

the further away from the equator, the more the sunlight spreads out

JUNE

Sun's rays hit straight on at equator

summer near North Pole

Costa Rica

winter near South Pole

no sunlight at South Pole

So how come Costa Rica just stays hot all year round?

Costa Rica is near the equator. Here, the sun's rays always hit the Earth straight on as it orbits the Sun.

SEASON CYCLE GOES AROUND
by Ariel Macaw

What's with all this
Hot and cold?
'Tis the seasons
so I'm told.
Costa Rican days remain
hot and moist; much the same.
Canada, on the other hand,
is a changing season land.
That's a temperate climate
for you: guaranteed
to never bore you.

Misty Morning

Next day, we were up before sunrise loading supplies into the *Mercury*. It was so chilly our breath made little clouds. Ariel and I warmed our wings on the hot blasts of air that Stork and Captain Goose blew into the balloon. Soon the *Mercury* was tugging at the rope that held it to the ground.

'Which way to Costa Rica?' I asked Stork.

'If we went straight to Costa Rica,' said Stork, 'we would have to pass along the east coast of America. At this time of year, violent storms rage up the coast – that's why it's often called "Hurricane Alley". We don't want to hit any storms, so we're going to travel through Europe, Africa, and back to Costa Rica.'

'Westerly wind's up,' quacked Captain Goose. 'Let's go!'

Stork released the rope and the *Mercury* lifted off the dewy ground into the cool morning air. Our great adventure had begun.

Hurricane Alley

sac for lighter-than-air helium gas

pan for burning fuel

books and maps

sac f hot a

Stork's weather laboratory

gondola

food and supplies

games and musical instruments

water and fuel

LIGHTER THAN AIR

🐦 *What makes this balloon fly? Its wings don't flap.*

🐦 Have you noticed how wood floats on top of water? That's because a block of wood is lighter than the same size 'block' of water. The same thing happens with different gases.

In the top sac of this balloon, there's helium gas, like in a toy balloon. Helium is lighter than the air around it, so it keeps the *Mercury* floating in the air. The other sac just has air in it. When we heat this air, it spreads out and takes up more space. This makes it lighter than the cold air outside, so the hot air rises and lifts the balloon with it.

🐦 *How do you drop back down?*

🐦 That's easy. Just let the air in the sac cool down. The air takes a little time to cool, so you have to plan ahead by a few minutes when you want to drop down.

lighter-than-air helium keeps balloon afloat

hot air lifts balloon up

FLOATING WATER

🐦 What a perfect morning for a take-off. Cloudless sky, nice and cool.

🐦 *Yeah, but it's wet. Where did all this water come from? Did it rain?*

🐦 It didn't rain, but last night was cold. Moisture in the air must have gathered on everything. That water is **dew.**

🐦 *Huh? Moisture in the air?*

🐦 The moisture in the air is **water vapour**. Water vapour is an invisible gas until it cools down and gathers, or **condenses**, into droplets of liquid water. Sometimes you see the air's moisture condense on the outside of a cold bottle.

🐦 *I always thought the drops on the outside of a cold bottle were because the drink was leaking out!*

SEE FOR YOURSELF
The Thirsty Air

You will need: ✳ a shallow bowl or dish

1 Half-fill the bowl with water.

2 Leave the dish indoors where it won't be disturbed.

 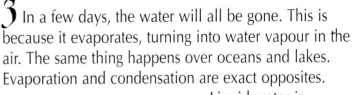

3 In a few days, the water will all be gone. This is because it evaporates, turning into water vapour in the air. The same thing happens over oceans and lakes. Evaporation and condensation are exact opposites.

Liquid water is constantly evaporating into water vapour and then condensing back into liquid.

The Big Squeezy

'Let's celebrate lift-off!' hollered Captain Goose. 'Sparrow, be a good egg, go below deck and bring up a bottle of bubbly drink.'

I poked around in the dark below deck, until one of the bags yelled, 'Ouch!'

'Hey, who's there?' I said.

A bulbous beak poked out of a bag saying, 'Ow, don't chuck me out! They're after me!'

'Who's after you?'

'The people from the Natural History Museum,' said the beak. 'They've been chasing me for weeks. Now they'll capture me, and it's all your fault!'

'Why are they chasing you?' I asked.

'Because I'm a dodo. People think dodos are extinct, but here I am, alive and kicking. They want to stick me in a glass case and put me on show to the public!'

'Well, they can't get you up here,' I piped. 'Grab that bubbly and come on up.'

AIR PRESSURE

Ow! My ears keep popping!

You haven't flown this high before, have you, Sparrow? You've been living at the bottom of a deep ocean of air – the Earth's atmosphere. The pressure of the atmosphere on this open book is the weight of a small car! Although you can't feel it, the weight of all that air on top of you squeezes you in all directions.

aeroplanes are filled with pressurized air to stop the pressure inside passengers' bodies from painfully pushing outwards

a weather vane points in the direction from which the wind is coming

So how come the pressure of the atmosphere doesn't just squash me flat?

Because your insides press back against the air around you. You don't even have to think about pushing out ... you're born with just the right pressure to fight the crush of the air.

What happens higher up?

The pressure becomes less until it drops to zero out in space, where there's no air. That's why astronauts wear air-tight space-suits. Have you seen what they look like floating in space?

Yeah, they look chubby and blown up in their space-suits – ha ha!

That's right – the suits are blown up with high-pressure air to make astronauts feel like they're surrounded by the Earth's atmosphere. Without this high-pressure air in their space-suits, astronauts would instantly explode in space.

Aw, cool! But what makes my ears hurt down here?

Your ears feel changes in air pressure. As the *Mercury* floats higher, the air pressure around you drops. But your ear pressure is the same as it was down on the ground. So your eardrums

pressure in ear

pressure outside

escape valve

push out more and more as we rise. Luckily, you have an escape valve between your middle ear and the back of your throat. When the air pressure in your ears gets big enough, some of the air in your middle ear 'pops' out through the escape valve.

Ow! There they pop again!

You don't have to wait for your ears to hurt and 'pop'. Swallowing usually opens your ears' escape valves. Here, suck on this sweet and it will help you swallow.

the helium sac in the *Mercury's* balloon will spread out, or expand, as it goes higher and higher in the atmosphere. If Captain Goose flew too high, it would pop!

SEE FOR YOURSELF
Atmosphere Pressing Everywhere

You will need:
* clear plastic cup
* index card, postcard, or thin piece of cardboard
* bathroom or kitchen sink

1 Fill the cup full of water.

2 Hold the cup of water over the sink. While holding the card against the rim of the cup, flip the cup upside down.

3 Gently let go of the card. It looks impossible, but the water doesn't spill out of the cup! The atmosphere is pressing up on the card. The pressure of the atmosphere is more than the weight of the water, so the water stays in the cup.

Stowaway!

Captain Goose squawked when Elmer the Dodo popped through the hatch.

'Good grief!' shouted Elmer. 'We're flying!'

'Flying all the way to Costa Rica – isn't that marvellous?' crowed Ariel.

'Costa Rica?' squawked Elmer. 'That's millions of miles away! Ow, get me down! Help!'

'Stop bawling,' said Captain Goose. 'You can easily fly to the ground at this height, can't you?'

'Silly goose – dodos can't fly! If this rattletrap falls apart, I'll drop like a bowling ball.'

ATMOSPHERE LEVELS

If the atmosphere is an ocean of air, will we float to the top of it?

Although the atmosphere seems to go on up for ever, it's really only a thin skin when compared to the size of the whole Earth. Imagine you shrunk the Earth to the size of a party balloon. Then the atmosphere would only be as thick as the balloon's rubber skin. We're going to fly very high, sometimes five miles above the Earth, but we'll still only be in the bottom layer of the atmosphere.

Gosh, the Earth is a lot bigger than I thought.

Scientists decided it was convenient to divide the atmosphere into imaginary layers. The divisions were chosen according to their temperature.

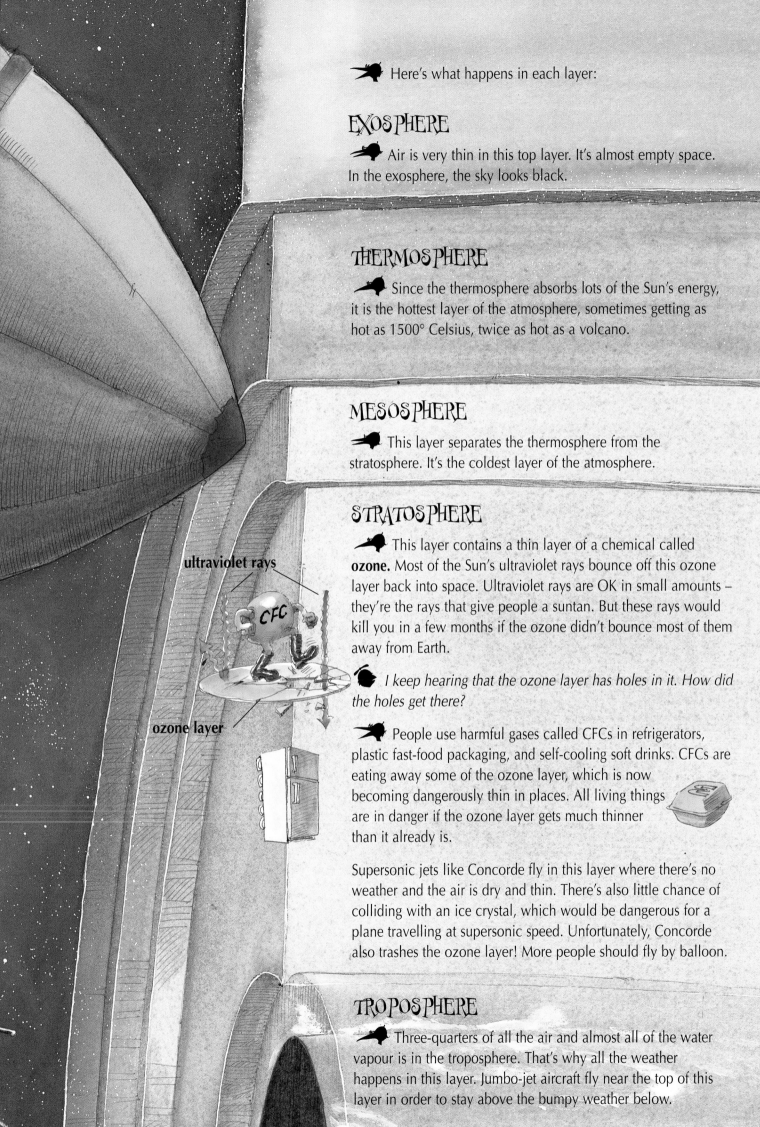

Here's what happens in each layer:

EXOSPHERE

Air is very thin in this top layer. It's almost empty space. In the exosphere, the sky looks black.

THERMOSPHERE

Since the thermosphere absorbs lots of the Sun's energy, it is the hottest layer of the atmosphere, sometimes getting as hot as 1500° Celsius, twice as hot as a volcano.

MESOSPHERE

This layer separates the thermosphere from the stratosphere. It's the coldest layer of the atmosphere.

STRATOSPHERE

This layer contains a thin layer of a chemical called **ozone.** Most of the Sun's ultraviolet rays bounce off this ozone layer back into space. Ultraviolet rays are OK in small amounts – they're the rays that give people a suntan. But these rays would kill you in a few months if the ozone didn't bounce most of them away from Earth.

I keep hearing that the ozone layer has holes in it. How did the holes get there?

People use harmful gases called CFCs in refrigerators, plastic fast-food packaging, and self-cooling soft drinks. CFCs are eating away some of the ozone layer, which is now becoming dangerously thin in places. All living things are in danger if the ozone layer gets much thinner than it already is.

Supersonic jets like Concorde fly in this layer where there's no weather and the air is dry and thin. There's also little chance of colliding with an ice crystal, which would be dangerous for a plane travelling at supersonic speed. Unfortunately, Concorde also trashes the ozone layer! More people should fly by balloon.

TROPOSPHERE

Three-quarters of all the air and almost all of the water vapour is in the troposphere. That's why all the weather happens in this layer. Jumbo-jet aircraft fly near the top of this layer in order to stay above the bumpy weather below.

ultraviolet rays

ozone layer

Gone with the Wind

Elmer is getting on everyone's nerves – he's so grouchy! Captain Goose threatens to put him in a barrel and send him over Niagara Falls.

It's far safer to float over the falls in the *Mercury*. In fact, the *Mercury* flies quite smoothly. It feels like we're standing still.

WIND

Professor, why don't I feel the wind blowing in the Mercury?

We're blowing along with the wind like a feather. If the *Mercury* got stuck in a tree and stopped, then you would feel the wind blowing past you.

What keeps on blowing us to the east? How are we ever going to turn around and travel west?

We can't go to Costa Rica in a straight line. We have to catch different winds. The first big wind we catch travels from west to east across the Atlantic Ocean. These big winds are called **prevailing winds.** Large prevailing winds are blowing constantly all over the globe.

THERE'S ALWAYS A WET **MIST** AT THE BOTTOM OF NIAGARA FALLS. IT LOOKS LIKE A CLOUD THAT GOT STUCK.

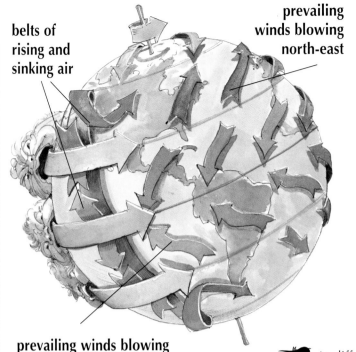

belts of rising and sinking air

prevailing winds blowing north-east

prevailing winds blowing towards equator

This wind map is like having a train map of the skies for balloon pilots.

Does this globe show all the wind blowing everywhere?

No, it leaves out all the small breezes. It only shows the larger prevailing winds. Winds near the Earth's surface are in red and purple, and the high-up winds are in green.

So how does Captain Goose steer the Mercury?

At different heights, the winds blow in slightly different directions. Down below us, there'll be a wind blowing in a different direction from the wind blowing us now. When Captain Goose wants the *Mercury* to change direction, he just lets the balloon cool down. It will sink into the layer below, and a different wind will blow us in a new direction.

What makes the wind blow?

Have you ever let air out of a toy balloon? You're letting the high pressure air squeezed in the balloon flow into the low pressure air outside the balloon. Wind always blows from high air-pressure areas to low air-pressure areas.

> HA! EVERYONE KNOWS THAT WIND IS CAUSED BY THE EARTH **BREATHING** IN AND OUT. EVEN THE ANCIENT **GREEKS** KNEW THAT.

ISOBARS

What are the black lines on your weather map?

They're called **isobars.** All the areas along this imaginary line are at the same air pressure.

So what do isobars tell you about weather?

When the isobars are squashed close together, this shows a steep change in pressure. Steep changes in pressure make strong winds.

So if I drew a map like this of Niagara Falls, the lines would be very close together where the water falls off the cliff.

wind blows across isobars

Hmmm, I suppose close isobars *are* sort of like the steep cliffs under Niagara Falls. Where the level of the cliff changes quickly, water flows quickly, just like the wind. Far-apart isobars mean pressure doesn't change much from one place to another. When isobars are far apart, breezes blow gently like a babbling brook.

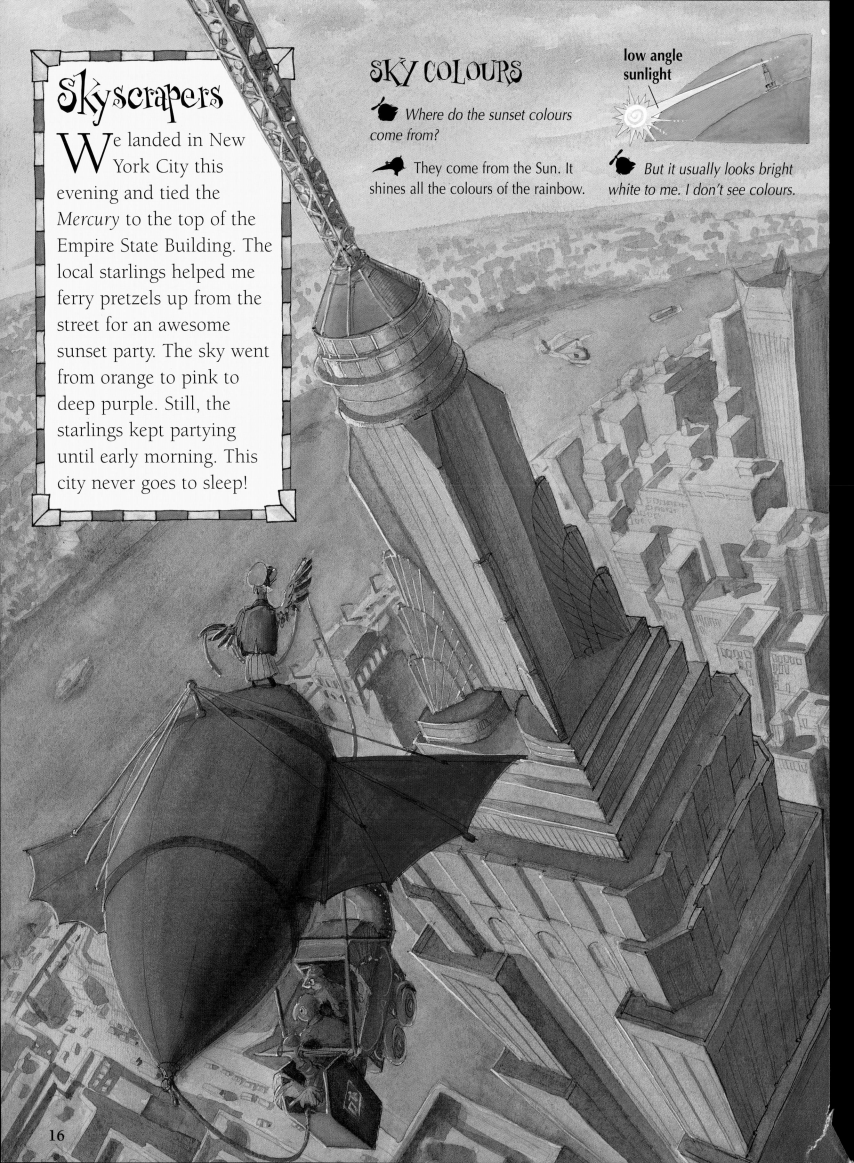

Skyscrapers

We landed in New York City this evening and tied the *Mercury* to the top of the Empire State Building. The local starlings helped me ferry pretzels up from the street for an awesome sunset party. The sky went from orange to pink to deep purple. Still, the starlings kept partying until early morning. This city never goes to sleep!

SKY COLOURS

Where do the sunset colours come from?

They come from the Sun. It shines all the colours of the rainbow.

But it usually looks bright white to me. I don't see colours.

low angle sunlight

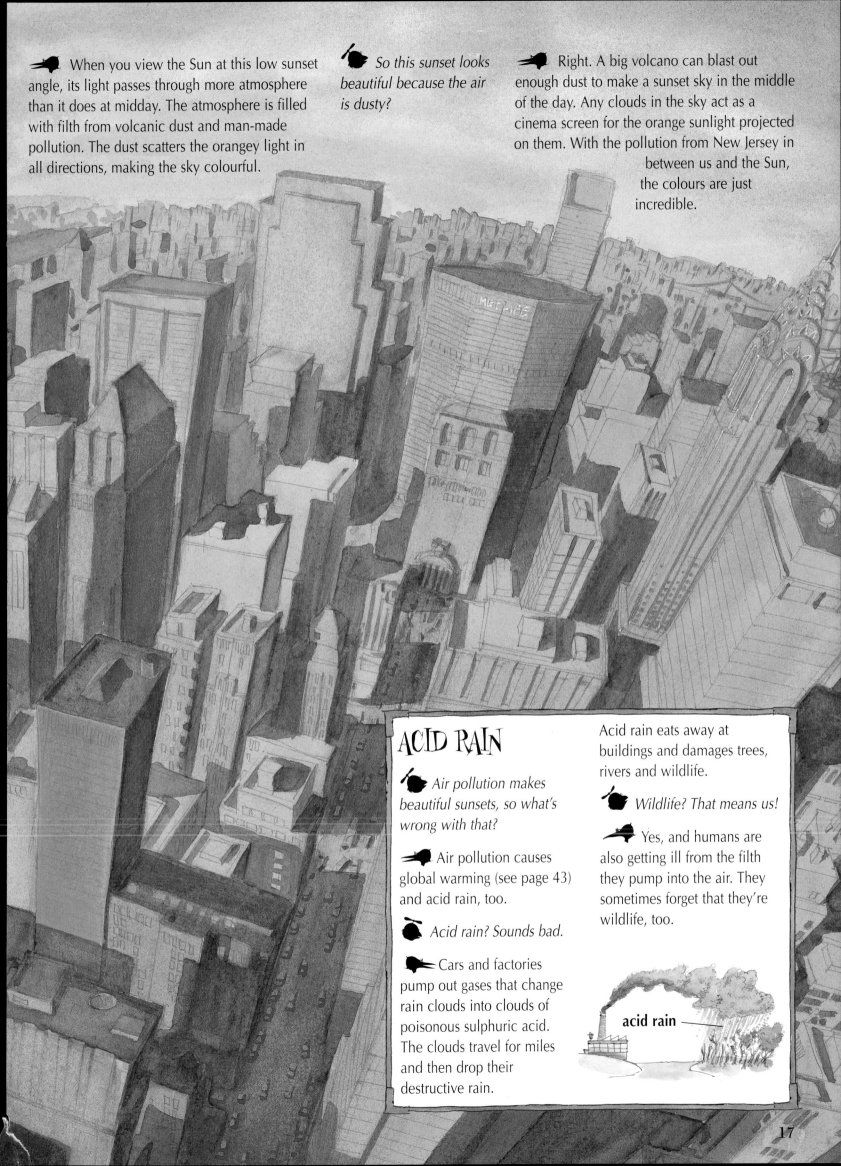

When you view the Sun at this low sunset angle, its light passes through more atmosphere than it does at midday. The atmosphere is filled with filth from volcanic dust and man-made pollution. The dust scatters the orangey light in all directions, making the sky colourful.

So this sunset looks beautiful because the air is dusty?

Right. A big volcano can blast out enough dust to make a sunset sky in the middle of the day. Any clouds in the sky act as a cinema screen for the orange sunlight projected on them. With the pollution from New Jersey in between us and the Sun, the colours are just incredible.

ACID RAIN

Air pollution makes beautiful sunsets, so what's wrong with that?

Air pollution causes global warming (see page 43) and acid rain, too.

Acid rain? Sounds bad.

Cars and factories pump out gases that change rain clouds into clouds of poisonous sulphuric acid. The clouds travel for miles and then drop their destructive rain.

Acid rain eats away at buildings and damages trees, rivers and wildlife.

Wildlife? That means us!

Yes, and humans are also getting ill from the filth they pump into the air. They sometimes forget that they're wildlife, too.

acid rain

A Cloud's Silver Lining

We left New York the next morning and started floating towards the Atlantic Ocean on a prevailing wind blowing from the west to the east.

'Cloud ahoy!' shouted Captain Goose. I'd never flown high enough to drop into a big fluffy cloud before. But just when we were about to hit the cloud, we were wrapped up in a damp fog.

What a dud!

CLOUDED VISION

Hey, what happened to the cloud?

You're inside it right now!

But it looked so nice and white and fluffy. It's wet and foggy in here.

Remember how the mist at Niagara Falls looked like a fluffy cloud? Clouds are made up of water droplets that have condensed around dust particles in the air. The droplets then hang around in the air like a clump of fog.

So what makes the cloud look white and fluffy outside?

Sunlight bounces off the droplets. This makes the cloud look fluffy white.

EVEN ON AN OVERCAST DAY, THE CLOUDS LOOK WHITE AND FLUFFY WHEN YOU VIEW THEM FROM ABOVE IN THE SUNSHINE

A CLOUD IS BORN

The sky was clear early this morning. Where did these clouds come from?

There are many different types of cloud and they all form differently. The cloud we're in now is called a **cumulus cloud**. It formed when the morning sun heated up air and water vapour near the ground. When this happened, huge blobs of warm moist air floated up. These blobs are called **thermals.**

sun heats blob of air below

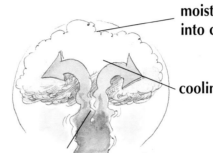

heated air blob (thermal) rises up

cloud has been cut into a cross-section to show the *Mercury* stuck inside

cloud looks like a thick fog when viewed from inside

When the thermals rose through the cool air higher up, they cooled down and billowed out like mushrooms. The moisture in the thermals condensed into tiny droplets. The droplets gathered around dust particles floating in the air.

moisture condenses into cumulus cloud

cooling air

thermal's hot moisture pushes through layer of cold air

Sometimes cumulus clouds look like they're all sitting on the same huge piece of glass. Why is that?

The clouds look flat underneath because this is the point where the warm thermals have 'blurped' their way through to the cool air higher up. The place where the warm and cool air meet is where the cloud looks as if it's sitting on glass.

Are clouds just floating water?

Yes. And the action of water condensing gives off heat. The cloud carries this heat far away from the area it came from. All clouds carry both water and heat from one place to another. You can think of clouds as great big sky taxis with water and heat as their passengers (see page 33).

YUK! IT'S WET UP HERE. THESE CLOUDS ARE SUPPOSED TO BE NICE AND SOFT!

SEE FOR YOURSELF
Pet Cloud

You will need:
* a large plastic drinks bottle
* an ice cube
* hot tap water

ice

real cloud

hot water

1 Fill the bottle one-third full of hot water.

2 Put the ice on top of the bottle.

3 Hot air rises above the hot water and floats into the bottle neck. Cold air drops down from the ice cube. The cold air makes the moisture in the hot air condense into a cloud. Your cloud won't be white and fluffy – it will look more like fog – but hey, it's a real cloud!

I SEE HORSE TAILS.

I SEE ANGEL'S HAIR AND ICE CREAM CASTLES IN THE AIR.

I SEE A U.F.O.

I SEE A NICE LOAF OF BREAD. HOW ABOUT YOU, PROFESSOR?

I SEE CONDENSED WATER DROPLETS REFLECTING SUNLIGHT. BEAUTIFUL!

VAPOUR TRAIL

Hot moist air blasting out of jet engines often leaves behind a 'vapour trail', a long thin frozen cirrus cloud.

CLOUD SHAPES

STRATUS

When the sky is grey and overcast, you can bet you're stuck under a stubborn stratus cloud pancake. Stratus clouds are huge cloud sheets. They appear when warm moist wind skims over a layer of cold air. Moisture in the warm wind condenses in the cold air so the stratus cloud might make mist or drizzle. Fog is a very low stratus cloud touching the ground.

Cloud Spotters

Professor Stork says you can 'read' clouds like a book. They tell you a lot about the weather to come.

Cloud names look like a real mouthful but they're only made up of a few bits of mix-and-match words. I used Captain Goose's deck of cards to help me keep track of the words and learn my cloud names.

WHITE 'SMOKE'

Sometimes the white 'smoke' you see belching out of a chimney is a man-made cloud. Hot, moist air from a chimney is like a thermal. The moist warm air rising makes long cumulus-like clouds.

 CIRRUS (means *wisp of hair*)

ALTO (means *high*)

 STRATUS (means *layer*)

NIMBO/NIMBUS (means *rain*)

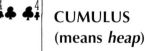 **CUMULUS** (means *heap*)

MAN-MADE (vapour trails and white 'smoke')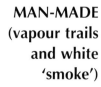

CIRRUS

When moisture condenses in freezing air, it freezes into ice crystals. Strong winds blow and stretch the ice crystal clouds into long wispy tails. Even on a hot day, you might still see frozen cirrus clouds high up in the atmosphere where it's always cold. Cirrus usually means a change in the weather.

CIRROSTRATUS

Cirrus clouds spread and blur into thin flat sheets.

Notice there are no cirronimbus clouds. Cirrus clouds are too high up and frozen to drop rain.

ALTOCUMULUS

Sometimes altocumulus clouds form what's called a 'mackerel sky' due to its fishy appearance. They usually mean a front is approaching (see page 24).

CUMULONIMBUS

These giant cumulus rain clouds usually mean thunderstorms are coming (see page 34).

STRATOCUMULUS

Stratocumulus are fluffier and less even than ordinary stratus. They're the most common type of cloud.

NIMBOSTRATUS

These flat blankets of rain clouds can drop steady rain for many days.

CROWDS OF CLOUDS
by Ariel Macaw

Cumulo~nimbus;
nimbo~stratus.
Nimbos rain
and nimbos splat us.
Nimbostratus can be found
half-a-mile above the ground,
while cumulonimbus,
rain-cloud king,
reigns to rain on everything,
and soak folks
'neath the troposphere
I wish they'd nimbo
out of here.

rain

Tears of a Cloud

We landed in London this evening after three days of sailing high over the Atlantic Ocean. I hope, now that we're over land, Elmer will stop singing those sea shanties!

The big dark cumulonimbus clouds that appeared this afternoon brought rain. But the people in Trafalgar Square were still outside giving food away. How lucky London pigeons are!

RAIN

Where does the rain come from?

From nimbus clouds. Remember what makes clouds?

Yes – tiny moisture droplets condensing in the air, right? (See page 19.)

Right. Most cumulonimbus clouds are cold enough to freeze the condensed droplets into little ice crystals. These ice crystals stick together and grow into bigger ice crystals.

When they are too big to float in the air, the crystals drop down. On their way to the ground, they melt into raindrops. Nimbostratus clouds are closer to the ground. Nimbostratus raindrops come from condensed droplets forming into bigger drops and then falling out of the sky. You could think of a raindrop as a tiny piece of a cloud landing on your head.

HAIL FREEZES OVER

Frozen ice crystals can build up into hailstones inside a violent thundercloud (see page 33). The crystals are blown up and down, building up layer upon layer of ice. I've seen hailstones bigger than golf balls drop down and smash up cars and rooftops and hurt people and animals.

Yes, and especially sparrows (sniff). I miss my Mama ...

You poor little dear (sniff). Now *we* are making raindrops too.

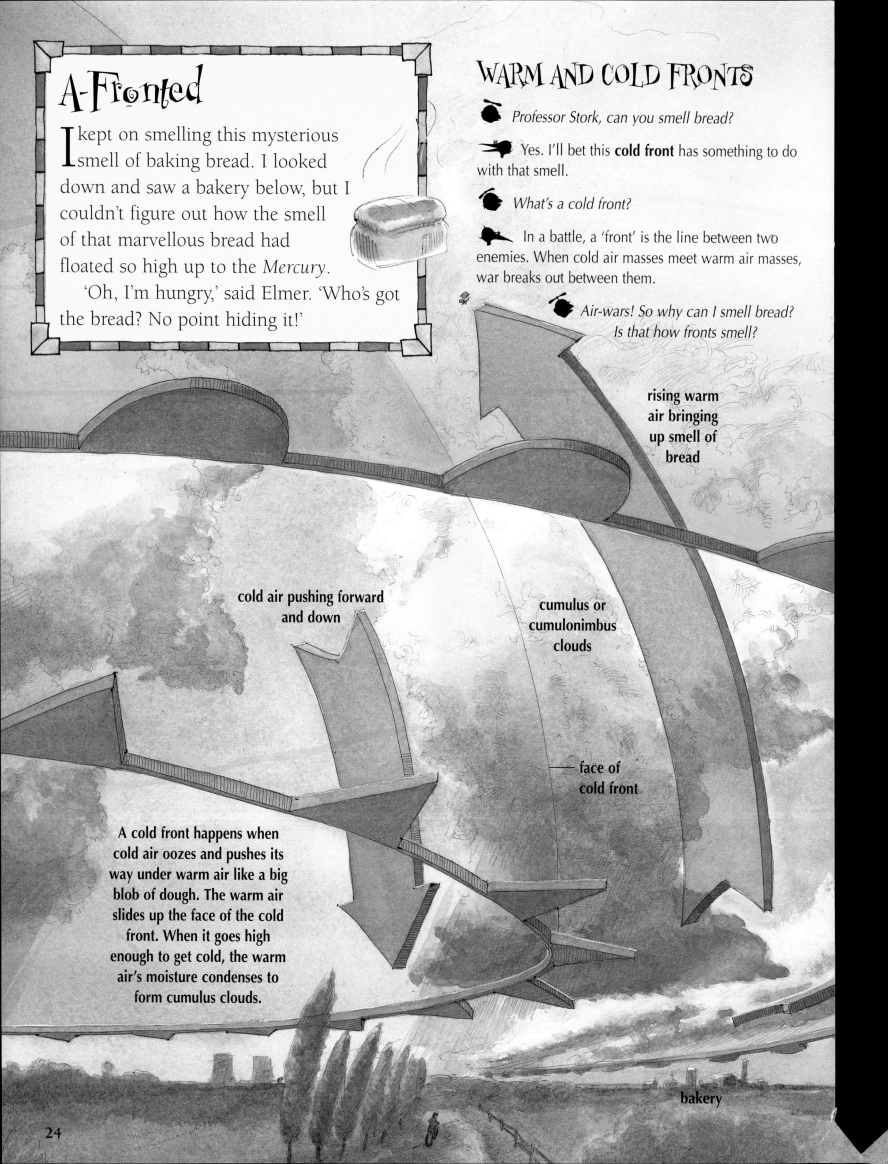

A-Fronted

I kept on smelling this mysterious smell of baking bread. I looked down and saw a bakery below, but I couldn't figure out how the smell of that marvellous bread had floated so high up to the *Mercury*.

'Oh, I'm hungry,' said Elmer. 'Who's got the bread? No point hiding it!'

WARM AND COLD FRONTS

Professor Stork, can you smell bread?

Yes. I'll bet this **cold front** has something to do with that smell.

What's a cold front?

In a battle, a 'front' is the line between two enemies. When cold air masses meet warm air masses, war breaks out between them.

Air-wars! So why can I smell bread? Is that how fronts smell?

rising warm air bringing up smell of bread

cold air pushing forward and down

cumulus or cumulonimbus clouds

face of cold front

A cold front happens when cold air oozes and pushes its way under warm air like a big blob of dough. The warm air slides up the face of the cold front. When it goes high enough to get cold, the warm air's moisture condenses to form cumulus clouds.

bakery

No, but can you see that bakery down underneath us? The smell of baking bread must have been carried up by the rising warm air along the face of a cold front.

But what happens to the weather along a front?

Fronts bring clouds and rain. So you can predict rainy weather if you know there's a front coming. Warm and cold fronts spiral around pockets of low pressure called **lows**. Often a cold front will follow a warm front, giving you rainy weather twice. Fortunately, cold front storms usually last only an hour or so.

cirrus clouds
followed by
stratus clouds

fronts circulate
around 'lows'

YOU LEAVE ME COLD, FRONT
by Ariel Macaw

Cold front,
   over me you've rolled,
      and left me cold.
You ooze along the ground
Like a great molasses mound.
You plough beneath warm air
   as if you didn't care
   about forcing warm air high
   like a thermal in the sky.
Don't you know this causes rain
   to shower on the plain?
If _that_ weren't bad enough,
   once you've dropped the stuff
   you briefly clear the skies,
   and then do it once again!

When warm air skims over a ramp of cold air, a warm front occurs. This warm air rises, cools, and forms clouds and rain.

cool air sliding
down beneath
warm front

face of
warm front

fronts travelling in this direction

25

The Alpine Mountain's Cold

We were tossed over the Alps on some speedy winds. The valleys were still green, but there was snow on top of the mountains even though it was only the end of October. Some clouds seemed to stick to one side of a mountain and stay there. The mountain weather was wild and unpredictable. It was so cold that Ariel had to stay inside the lower sac in the balloon.

MOUNTAIN WEATHER

It's so weird how the weather on one side of a mountain is so different from weather on the other side.

Not only do mountains have a wetter and a drier side, but one side may be in shadow most of the time while the other side gets more sun. The warm sunny side of the mountain can appear to be in a totally different season compared to the cold shadowy side.

How do mountains affect the weather?

These mountains almost create their own weather. Mountains stick up above the land around them where the air is cold, dry and windy. Remember how when air gets colder, it holds less moisture?

Sure, and so moisture in the air condenses.

Right, and when warm moist air from the valley blows up one side of the mountain, the moisture condenses in the cold air near the mountain top. That makes the fog and clouds which bring precipitation on the mountain slopes.

'Precipitation'? What's that?

Precipitation is a word for any form of water that falls from the clouds – rain, snow or hail. Any warm moist air that gets pushed up into the cold air doesn't stand a chance – rain and snow just get squeezed out of it. This usually makes one side of the mountain rainy or snowy and the other side of the mountain very dry.

this side of the mountain has rain and snow most of the time

dry air blowing into the valley

cold air sinks from mountain tops down into valleys at night, condensing nearby moisture into clouds and fog

mountains squeeze moisture out of the air

when the sun shines, warm air in valleys rises up mountain slopes, making clouds

26

SNOW

In these mountains, you blink your eyes and the weather's changed. It's sunny where we are, but you can see the snow falling over on that side of the mountain.

When does a rain cloud become a snow cloud?

Water vapour freezes around bits of dust. It makes ice crystals that bunch together, and that makes snowflakes. The snowflakes always have six sides, but each snowflake looks slightly different.

There's so much snow on these mountain tops. It looks like it's piled higher than a house in places.

Snow piles up ten times higher than it would if it dropped as rain instead because air is trapped between the snowflakes. The snow looks white because snow crystals reflect white sunlight like little diamonds.

Catching Breath in Venice

Over the Alps to Italy, we floated into Venice. We moored up to a lamppost on the banks of the lagoon. Venice is a very strange city. Instead of streets, there are canals, and the pigeons were being fed – this time by a government official! There were some scary-looking winged lions around, but they stood very still and luckily didn't seem to notice us.

COASTAL WEATHER

Have you noticed that the wind is blowing in the opposite direction from the way it was blowing during the daytime?

Oh yeah – today the wind blew in from the sea. Now the wind is blowing out to sea.

During the day, the air above the land is hotter than it is above water. Guess where thermals will be rising quickest.

Over the ground, of course, because the air's hotter. The hot air rises.

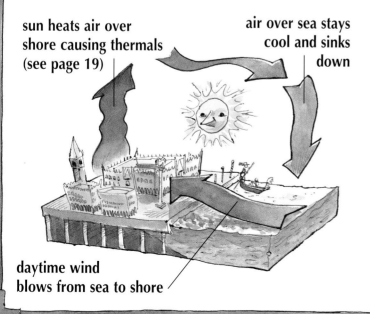

sun heats air over shore causing thermals (see page 19)

air over sea stays cool and sinks down

daytime wind blows from sea to shore

Right. And you know wind blows from high to low pressure (see page 15). The rising thermals above the land leave an area of low pressure that sucks the sea breeze in from over the ocean.

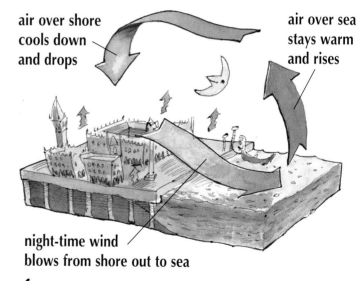

air over shore cools down and drops

air over sea stays warm and rises

night-time wind blows from shore out to sea

So why does the wind change direction at night?

At night, the land cools down faster than the ocean does. So the air over the land is then cooler than the air over the ocean. Warm air over the ocean keeps rising, leaving areas of low pressure just on top of the ocean. The heavier, cooler air over the land is drawn out into the low-pressure area over the ocean. It's usually windy at the seaside because of the way the land heats up and cools down more quickly than the ocean.

Deserting a Sinking Ship

It's been two weeks since we left Venice. We travelled across the Mediterranean Sea and over Africa's Sahara Desert. The desert weather bounced between extremes. In the daytime, it was extremely hot. Our hot-air balloon didn't float so well when the air around it was also hot, so we kept dragging on the ground.

OH FOR A **PARK** FOUNTAIN

Then, as soon as the Sun set, it got extremely cold. We floated for days without a drop of water. We were all parched and exhausted.

A vulture wheeled around the *Mercury*, spying us with a greedy eye. 'Bring out your dead!' he called. 'Say, isn't that a dodo on board? They're extinct ... he has to have been dead for years! Come on, fork him over!' The vulture dived into the gondola and pecked at Elmer.

'Go away!' shrieked Ariel. 'We're practically dying of thirst. We don't need any more trouble.'

'Oh, please die soon. I'm so hungry,' said the vulture.

'We're hungry, too,' said Stork. 'I could kill for a nice wriggly fish. But I wouldn't stoop so low as to eat a fellow bird.'

'Even if it were only a dodo,' added Captain Goose.

'Fish? Ha!' spat the vulture. 'You're hundreds of miles from the African coast. But the Niger River isn't far away. You can have a good drink. It's popular with the desert foxes. Watch out for them, or I may be eating your leftovers later on!'

DESERT WEATHER

Why does the desert get so hot in the day and so cold at night?

Remember in Venice (see page 28) how the ground heated up and cooled down more quickly than the water in the ocean? Here in the desert, there's very little water in the air or the ground. So the dry desert land and air heat up very quickly in the day and cool down very quickly at night.

So, without moisture in the air, clouds won't form over the desert.

And that lets the heat from the ground escape into space. You see, clouds make a cosy blanket that traps the heat given off by the ground and keeps the night air warm. Here in the desert, there's no blanket of clouds to keep the ground warm. Every night is a cold one.

How do deserts become so dry in the first place?

There are several reasons. Sometimes mountains squeeze almost all the moisture out of the air on one side, leaving the other side a dry desert.

Other deserts form because they're far from an ocean where the air could pick up moisture. These sort of deserts are often in the middle of big continents.

Some deserts form where dry sinking air falls all the time. This makes a high-pressure area with little rainfall. That's what's happening here in the Sahara. You can see that there are large deserts which lie just where the prevailing winds collide and push down. That makes the high pressure and the dry hot *climate*.

I'd hate to be here in summer or winter. Can you imagine how extreme the temperatures must be then?

Yes, the highest temperature ever recorded was in Libya in 1922. It hit 58° Celsius – that's 136.4° Fahrenheit, hot enough to slow-cook a chicken!

prevailing winds collide and push down to make this desert

31

Storm A-brewin'

We made it to Sierra Leone, on the coast of West Africa. I was very glad to get out of the desert. It's a place fit for camels but not for thirsty birds. From now on I won't think of rain as a curse but as a blessing.

The air was hot and steaming with moisture. We hung in the scorching air, roasting like ducks.

'This heat is killing me,' moaned Captain Goose, who was cooking in his uniform. 'We could sure use some rain to cool things down.'

'Well, we have the ingredients for a whopping good tropical storm,' said Professor Stork. 'Hot sun, moist air.'

Elmer butted in, 'And plenty of hot air from you two.'

'Blow me,' cried Captain Goose, 'we're in a blasted cumulonimbus! (See page 21.) Let's hope it doesn't become a thunderstorm, or we could be five charred-black birds baked in the sky.' But just as he spoke, there came an ominous deep rumble.

STORM CLOUDS

Gasp – it's so hot and sticky, I think I'm going to pass out.

I expect this very hot sun will produce some strong thermals. They will push cumulus clouds very high into the sky and make a fast upward wind called an **updraught.**

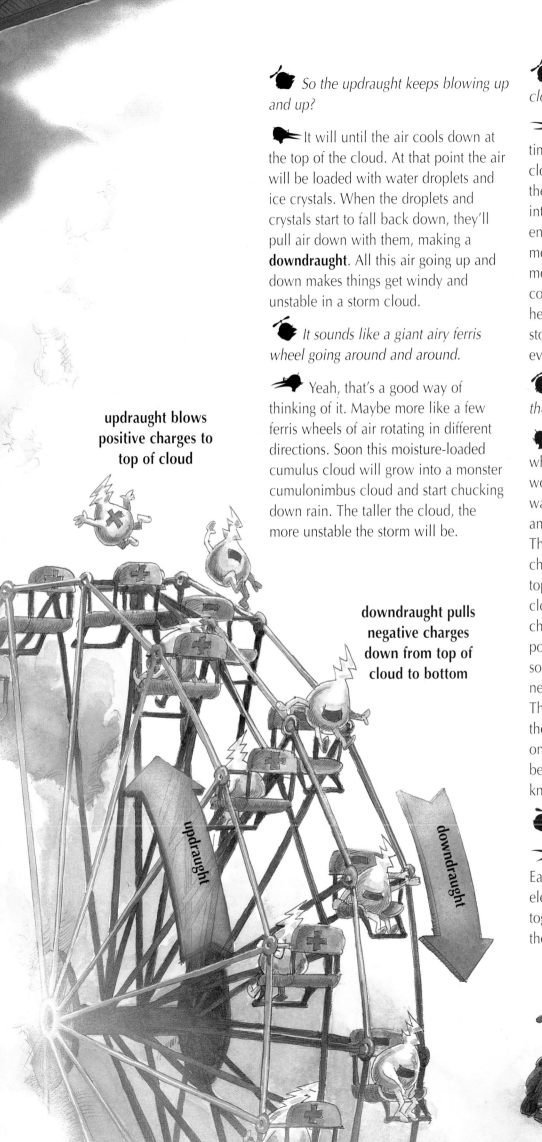

updraught blows positive charges to top of cloud

downdraught pulls negative charges down from top of cloud to bottom

updraught

downdraught

🐦 *So the updraught keeps blowing up and up?*

🐦 It will until the air cools down at the top of the cloud. At that point the air will be loaded with water droplets and ice crystals. When the droplets and crystals start to fall back down, they'll pull air down with them, making a **downdraught**. All this air going up and down makes things get windy and unstable in a storm cloud.

🐦 *It sounds like a giant airy ferris wheel going around and around.*

🐦 Yeah, that's a good way of thinking of it. Maybe more like a few ferris wheels of air rotating in different directions. Soon this moisture-loaded cumulus cloud will grow into a monster cumulonimbus cloud and start chucking down rain. The taller the cloud, the more unstable the storm will be.

🐦 *Where does all this cloud power come from?*

🐦 Once upon a time, the water in this cloud evaporated from the oceans and the ground. When the water changed into water vapour, it took some heat energy with it. When water vapour moves through the air, its heat energy moves with it. Then when water vapour condenses into clouds, it gives off this heat energy. The energy brewing up this storm could have come from water that evaporated off a distant ocean.

🐦 *Maybe we will get a big thunderstorm.*

🐦 Nobody really knows for sure what makes a thunderstorm, but I think it works like this: inside a thundercloud, water droplets and ice crystals hurl up and down on those air 'ferris wheels'. The wheels carry electric charges between the top and bottom of the cloud. Some charges are positive (+) and some are negative (–). This causes the thermosphere way above the cloud to be electrically charged in one way, say positive, and the Earth to be charged in the other way. Do you know what opposite charges like to do?

🐦 *Uh, I've heard opposites attract.*

🐦 Exactly. The thermosphere and the Earth load up with opposite charges. The electric force pulling the charges back together gets enormous. And that's when the fun begins.

FUN? I'LL KEEP MY FEATHERS CROSSED.

Lightning Strikes...But Where?

'These cumulonimbus clouds near the equator are the biggest in the world,' said Professor Stork. 'It looks like we're in for a mighty thunderstorm.' There was a flash, and then the deep booming sound of thunder.

Elmer squawked, 'Look, there's an old church. Lightning wouldn't *dare* strike a church. That should be a safe place to tie up until the storm ends! Hurry up, Captain – what are you waiting for?'

'For once, you're right, Elmer,' said Captain Goose. 'We're mooring up, folks!'

Stork looked alarmed. 'If we tie up to that steeple, we'll be the highest thing sticking out of the ground – a likely target for a bolt of lightning. Believe me, we'd be better off just floating through the storm.'

'Nuts!' said Elmer, as he threw the rope around the church steeple.

LIGHTNING AND THUNDER

🐦 *What's lightning made of that it can actually kill somebody?*

🦅 Lightning is electricity. In a fraction of a second, a lightning bolt releases enough energy to light up a big city for hours. The energy in a cumulonimbus cloud can make one heck of a megashock.

🐦 *How does the cloud do that?*

🦅 Here's how it works:

1. A strong electric force pulls between the separated positive and negative electric charges (see page 33). Soon, the force gets so strong

that **ZAP!** the charges suddenly zoom together and blast through the air.

2. Lightning can flash between the ground and the cloud or within a cloud. The bolt you see is caused by charges zipping from the ground to the thundercloud and back. This can happen many times in a split second.

3. Hot lightning roasts the air around it. This heat explosion makes the boom of thunder.

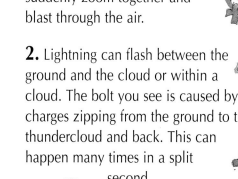
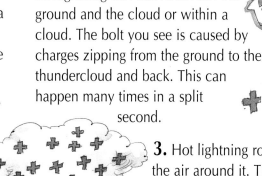

separated opposite charges pull on each other

🐦 *So that's where that heat energy ends up! (See page 33.)*

🦅 Indeed. A lightning bolt is five times as hot as the Sun's surface.

🐦 *How does lightning decide where to strike?*

🦅 Lightning takes the shortest route between two points, usually between the ground and the sky. That's why it leaps off tall trees, church steeples and skyscrapers.

🐦 *But, on top of this steeple, we're the highest thing around right now!*

🦅 I know. We'd be much better off getting away from this church and

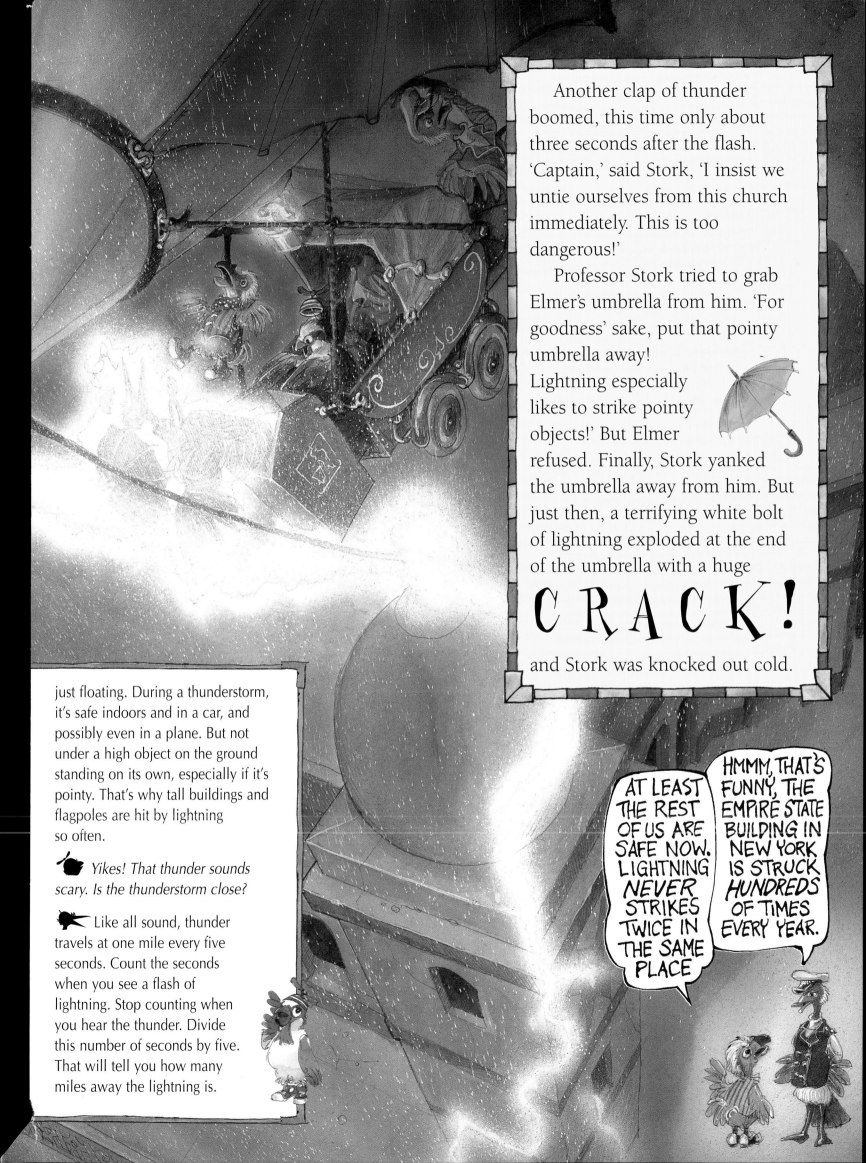

Another clap of thunder boomed, this time only about three seconds after the flash. 'Captain,' said Stork, 'I insist we untie ourselves from this church immediately. This is too dangerous!'

Professor Stork tried to grab Elmer's umbrella from him. 'For goodness' sake, put that pointy umbrella away! Lightning especially likes to strike pointy objects!' But Elmer refused. Finally, Stork yanked the umbrella away from him. But just then, a terrifying white bolt of lightning exploded at the end of the umbrella with a huge

CRACK!

and Stork was knocked out cold.

just floating. During a thunderstorm, it's safe indoors and in a car, and possibly even in a plane. But not under a high object on the ground standing on its own, especially if it's pointy. That's why tall buildings and flagpoles are hit by lightning so often.

Yikes! That thunder sounds scary. Is the thunderstorm close?

Like all sound, thunder travels at one mile every five seconds. Count the seconds when you see a flash of lightning. Stop counting when you hear the thunder. Divide this number of seconds by five. That will tell you how many miles away the lightning is.

AT LEAST THE REST OF US ARE SAFE NOW. LIGHTNING NEVER STRIKES TWICE IN THE SAME PLACE

HMMM, THAT'S FUNNY, THE EMPIRE STATE BUILDING IN NEW YORK IS STRUCK HUNDREDS OF TIMES EVERY YEAR.

Dull Daze in the Haze

The thunderstorm blew us further and further out to sea. Stork was alive but very ill and was sleeping all the time. Stuck floating on the ocean, we were getting very hungry.

Days later it became eerily still and foggy. I was fishing when I saw a giant white albatross circling down towards us. 'Ahoy,' I called. 'We're stuck here! Where has all the wind gone?'

'Wind?' he chuckled. 'You're in the doldrums, dude! No wind out here!'

Captain Goose snapped at me, 'Never talk to an albatross! Bad luck for sailors.'

'Tell him to buzz off,' piped Elmer.

'Don't be so superstitious!' I said. 'Stork would ask him for help!'

'Yar, dudes,' said the albatross, 'down here in the doldrums, the wind doesn't blow, but there's some awesome

THE DOLDRUMS

🦜 *Why doesn't the wind blow around here? Where did it all go?*

🦅 Prevailing winds blow from the north and the south, and here they crash into each other head-on. All the wind shoots straight up. That makes updraughts up high – awesome for air-surfing! But it strands all you non-surfin' fools down here where there's no wind at all.

🦜 *Kinda hard to believe there's wind anywhere right now.*

🦅 Well, you've got air rising in one place and falling down somewhere else. That makes huge bands of wind going around and around. You just happen to be stuck under a place where two of the bands are blowing wind straight up.

no wind down here

surfing a few thousand metres up. Up there, you can catch a good wind that blows you clear to Costa Rica.'

'That's my home!' chimed Ariel.

'Buzz off, surfer boy!' shouted Elmer. 'Go pester a pirate ship.'

'Never mind the dodo,' I said to the albatross. 'None of us do.'

'Dodo?' piped the albatross. 'I thought you dodo dudes were gonzo, man! Look, y'all are gonna *toast* out here without some help. I'll go get some righteous dudes to bail you out.'

An hour later, the albatross was back with nine others. 'Hang six!' he shouted.

The gang grabbed hold of the *Mercury* and flapped their wings furiously. They yanked the *Mercury* out of the water.

In minutes, we were shooting up in an updraught. 'Thank you, Albatross! And well done, Sparrow!' bellowed Captain Goose. 'Thank Saint Christopher you made friends with this gang!'

perpetual clouds over doldrums occur near equator

rising air

That sounds like the opposite of what happened in the desert. The prevailing winds crashed into each other and pushed dry air down (see page 31).

Aw, man – I hate downdraughts! But here, moist air rises up all the time. When it cools down, the moisture condenses into water. That's why the sky is so hazy. Sometimes you even get some bad thunderstorms.

Has it been doing this for long?

Oh yeah, my great-great-great-grand-daddy surfed here until he was shot down by some crazy sailor dude. Years ago when people used to travel in sailing ships, being stranded here really freaked out the sailors. They were superstitious and thought albatrosses were bad luck!

'TWAS I WHO SHOT THE ALBATROSS!

Eye of the Hurricane

We drifted west on the high winds north of the equator. It was very windy, so we moved along at great speed. Best of all, Stork was pretty much back to her old self again.

But the next day, the wind kept getting stronger and it started to rain. 'It's hopeless,' said Captain Goose. 'We'll have to ride this storm out. What do you make of this one, Storkie?'

'I think it's a hurricane forming,' said Stork.

'You mean a typhoon?' said Captain Goose.

'Typhoon, hurricane, cyclone ... call it what you like – they're all powerful storms,' said Stork.

An hour later, the sky right above us became clear. But the storm spiralled all around us.

'Look up!' shouted Captain Goose. 'We're in the bloomin' eye of the hurricane.'

Up and up we rocketed until finally we flew out of the top of the hurricane.

HURRICANES

There's plenty of moisture over the ocean to keep feeding this storm. Water must be evaporating off those hot tropical oceans like crazy. As water condenses into liquid droplets forming clouds, it gives out heat. The extra heat makes the air rise even faster, sucking in warm air.

Golly, and here we're miles away from land – will that make things worse?

I'm afraid so. Hurricanes don't die out easily until they strike land.

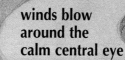

winds blow around the calm central eye

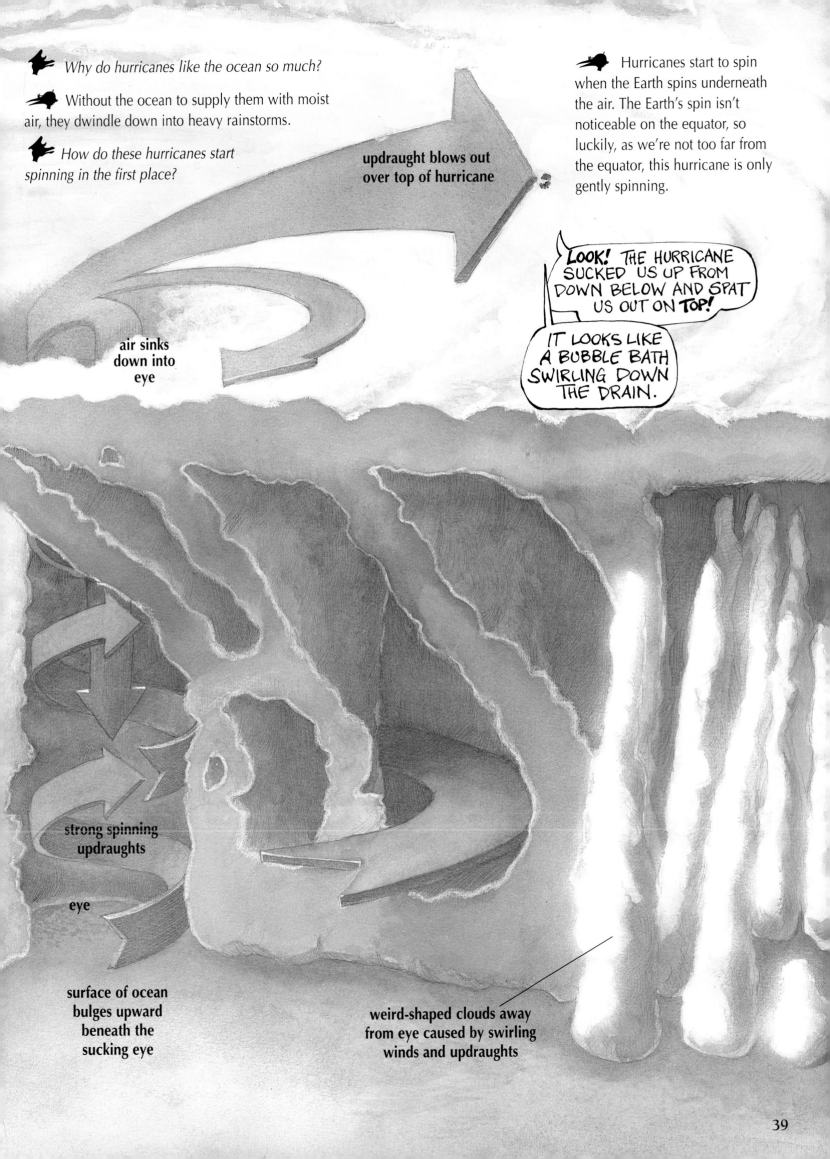

Why do hurricanes like the ocean so much?

Without the ocean to supply them with moist air, they dwindle down into heavy rainstorms.

How do these hurricanes start spinning in the first place?

Hurricanes start to spin when the Earth spins underneath the air. The Earth's spin isn't noticeable on the equator, so luckily, as we're not too far from the equator, this hurricane is only gently spinning.

updraught blows out over top of hurricane

air sinks down into eye

LOOK! THE HURRICANE SUCKED US UP FROM DOWN BELOW AND SPAT US OUT ON **TOP!**

IT LOOKS LIKE A BUBBLE BATH SWIRLING DOWN THE DRAIN.

strong spinning updraughts

eye

surface of ocean bulges upward beneath the sucking eye

weird-shaped clouds away from eye caused by swirling winds and updraughts

Here Be Dragons!

On the fortieth day of our journey, Elmer was on lookout. All of a sudden he shouted out, 'Oh no!'

'You're supposed to say "Land ho", bozo,' said Captain Goose.

'It's not land,' cried Elmer. 'It's a dragon! We're at the edge of the world!'

Professor Stork looked through the spyglass. 'I think those bumps are hills on an island, Elmer.'

'I *know* those are hills, dummy!' cried Elmer. 'I'm talking about that monster over *there*! We're dead ducked!'

It looked as if Elmer was right this time. I could see the enormous neck of the giant sea monster and hear its dreadful roaring.

'That's no dragon,' said Professor Stork. 'That's a tornado!'

The tornado foamed and sucked up dirt like a gigantic hoover. The huge dark funnel left the island and hit the ocean. It sucked up water and debris. It swept by only a few hundred metres away from us.

Have you ever seen it raining fish? Would you believe it, that's just what happened next. Fish after glorious fish splattered all over the deck!

'Mackerel from heaven!' crowed Captain Goose.

air flowing downward in eye

upward spiralling winds around eye

eye of tornado

condensation

water being sucked up

TORNADOES AND WATERSPOUTS

Where did these fish come from?

The tornado brought them! When the tornado drifted over the ocean, it became a waterspout. It sucked up the fish in the sea like a giant vacuum cleaner and dropped them on us, all fresh and wriggling.

How come the tornado turned from brown to white when it drifted over the ocean?

When tornadoes strike over land, they're the colour of the dirt they suck up. The whiteness was caused by water condensing in the waterspout, and ocean water being sucked up into the air.

How do tornadoes start?

Tornadoes form in thunderclouds. Sometimes, a thunderstorm's updraughts and downdraughts become unusually strong. The updraughts suck up the air so quickly that air near the ground rushes in to take its place. The air rushing in spirals very slightly, due to the spinning of the Earth. When the in-rushing air gets sucked into the tornado itself, the spinning becomes incredibly fast. The same thing happens to water when it swirls down the drain.

debris
colours
tornado

water swirls slowly

water swirls quickly

Water far from the drain swirls slowly, while water near the drain swirls quickly.

How fast does the wind blow in a tornado?

Sometimes a tornado's winds blow over 250 miles per hour. We made it through the hurricane, but you wouldn't want to get sucked up by a waterspout or a tornado ... they're much more powerful suckers. They can pick up cars and smash them like toys.

Oh, so Dorothy's house really could have been sucked into the air by a tornado, like in The Wizard of Oz?

Easily. But I don't suppose anyone could really end up 'over the rainbow' (see page 44).

Land Ho!

We floated over the Caribbean Sea for another day. We had plenty of fish and we ate like pigeons until we could hardly move.

Captain Goose was the first bird to spot Costa Rica. 'Land ho!' he shouted. As we drifted near, I could see the huge forest of giant trees buried in mist.

'It's home! We've done it!' cried Ariel. She was so excited, she laid an egg, right then and there.

OXYGEN AND WATER CYCLES

My rainforest is so beautiful. I thought I'd never see it again.

I've always wanted to see a rainforest myself. Rainforest plants drink in rainwater and carbon dioxide from the air to make their own food. Then they give off water vapour and oxygen.

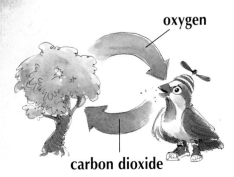

oxygen

carbon dioxide

Yes, it's so nice to breathe that fresh moist air.

All living things breathe in oxygen and breathe out carbon dioxide, which plants need to make food. Humans pump loads of carbon dioxide into the atmosphere when they burn fuel in their cars and factories. It's important that the rainforest survives to convert all this extra carbon dioxide back into oxygen.

Why is that so important?

Carbon dioxide is one of the main greenhouse gases that cause global warming. These gases trap the Sun's heat, preventing it from escaping into space.

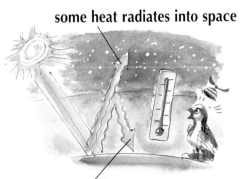

some heat radiates into space

greenhouse gases trap heat

If the atmosphere continues to heat up, the giant ice caps at the North and South Poles will start to melt and the oceans will expand because of the heat. These two factors will raise the levels of the oceans. This would cause flooding and changes in the weather.

Why is it so foggy around the rainforest? It looks like a cloud got stuck in all the leaves.

The moisture that the rainforest plants spew out makes a fog. It can 'rain' in the middle of the rainforest even if the skies above are sunny.

Where does all the water come from? Won't it ever run out?

The same water has been cycling around the world for millions of years. In every glass of water, some water particles will once have been drunk by a dinosaur – and some water particles will have been urinated into the Nile by an ancient Egyptian.

water evaporates from ground

Yechh! That's gross.

Ah, but only the pure water in the urine evaporates from the rivers and oceans, leaving the nasty stuff behind. When you drink, sweat and pee, you join in the great global water cycle.

Rembrandt of the Rain

Ariel had finally returned home and word spread quickly through the rainforest; parrots can really yak! By morning, cousins and friends had flown in from miles around. We all went out and dug up the biggest, juiciest wiggly worms in the world.

It rained for a while in the afternoon. But it stopped just in time for our beach party. And to top things off, there was a gleaming rainbow. 'Quick!' Elmer shrieked. 'There'll be a pot of gold at the end of that rainbow! I'm rich!' He scurried off down the beach.

We never saw Elmer ever again.

RAINBOW

Where do all those beautiful rainbow colours come from?

If the Sun is shining and the rain is falling in the opposite part of the sky, you might see a rainbow if you stand with your back to the Sun. Sunlight is made up of all the colours of the rainbow. Usually you can't see the colours because they all combine to make white light. You can only see the colours if they are separated.

So how do the colours become separated?

Raindrops act like tiny lenses that bend sunlight and reflect its colours separately. Red light bends the least, while blue-violet light bends the most.

blue light seen coming from drops like this

red light seen coming from drops like this

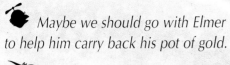

Maybe we should go with Elmer to help him carry back his pot of gold.

Pshaw! That old 'pot of gold' story! Take ten steps towards the rainbow. What happens?

Hey, it moved away!

It looks like it moved away, but actually, you're now seeing a slightly different rainbow. Now you can see light reflected by different drops from before. Each of us sees our own private rainbow in a slightly different place. It only *seems* as though we're all looking at the same rainbow.

So Elmer is going to run and run chasing that rainbow, and it will just move further and further away from him?

Yup, until the sky dries up or the Sun goes down – then the rainbow will disappear. He's going to miss out on all the fun just because his head is so darn full of superstitious rubbish. I won't miss him, will you?

Naw ...

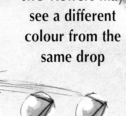

two viewers may see a different colour from the same drop

each viewer sees their own rainbow

SEE FOR YOURSELF
Make Your Own Rainbow

You will need: * a garden hose fitted with a spray nozzle (or a plant sprayer filled with water)

1 On a sunny day, stand with your back to the Sun and turn on the hose.

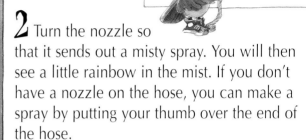

2 Turn the nozzle so that it sends out a misty spray. You will then see a little rainbow in the mist. If you don't have a nozzle on the hose, you can make a spray by putting your thumb over the end of the hose.

If you try this experiment using a plant sprayer, be sure to do it out of doors.

HEY, I THOUGHT DODOS WERE **EXTINCT**.

SHH! YOU'LL HURT HIS FEELINGS.

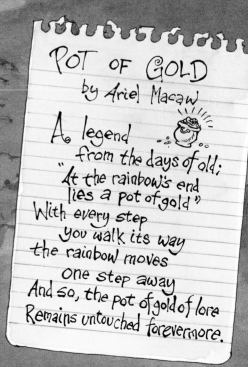

POT OF GOLD
by Ariel Macaw

A legend from the days of old:
"At the rainbow's end lies a pot of gold"
With every step you walk its way
the rainbow moves one step away
And so, the pot of gold of lore
Remains untouched forevermore.

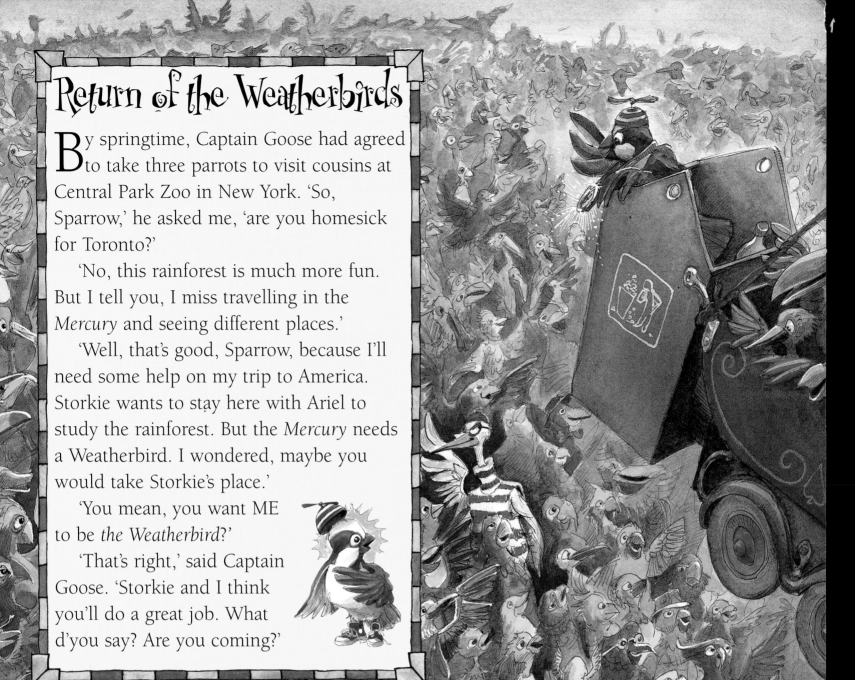

Return of the Weatherbirds

By springtime, Captain Goose had agreed to take three parrots to visit cousins at Central Park Zoo in New York. 'So, Sparrow,' he asked me, 'are you homesick for Toronto?'

'No, this rainforest is much more fun. But I tell you, I miss travelling in the *Mercury* and seeing different places.'

'Well, that's good, Sparrow, because I'll need some help on my trip to America. Storkie wants to stay here with Ariel to study the rainforest. But the *Mercury* needs a Weatherbird. I wondered, maybe you would take Storkie's place.'

'You mean, you want ME to be *the Weatherbird*?'

'That's right,' said Captain Goose. 'Storkie and I think you'll do a great job. What d'you say? Are you coming?'

FORECASTING TIPS

A Weatherbird can make a pretty good guess as to how the weather will change. Here are a few useful tools and tips.

Barometer
measures air pressure

low pressure = rainy weather   **high pressure = fair weather**

Hygrometer
measures moisture in the air

If the air is damp, it must be packed with moisture. Moisture usually means unstable weather ahead. Hot and sticky days often end with a rainstorm. In this little house hygrometer, a thin hair holds up the platform with the two figures. The hair stretches when the air is moist and this makes the blue 'rain man' pop out. A fresh pine cone also makes a pretty good hygrometer. When it dries out, it opens up. When it's damp, the scales close up.

Thermometer
measures temperature

Very high temperatures can boil up massive thermals and make afternoon thunderstorms if there's enough moisture in the air. Very low temperatures, well below 0° Celsius, usually mean dry weather.

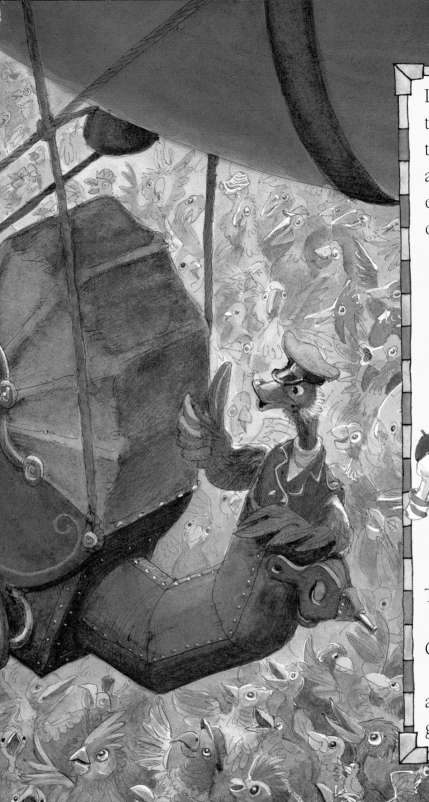

Later that week, Captain Goose, the three Costa Ricans and I boarded for the trip to New York. Ariel's friends and family gathered to see us off. Professor Stork appeared out of the crowd.

SPARROW, NOW THAT YOU'RE THE WEATHERBIRD, I WANT YOU TO HAVE MY COMPASS. IT'S FOR KEEPS.

NOW, DON'T FORGET TO READ THE CLOUDS

I'LL READ THE CLOUDS

AND WATCH FOR FRONTS

I'LL WATCH FOR FRONTS

AND REMEMBER YOUR HIGHS AND LOWS. GOOD LUCK, SPARROW. WATCH THE SKY!

Then Stork disappeared into the crowd.

'Ready to lift off, Sparrow!' honked Captain Goose.

'Aye, Cap'n,' I said. I untied the rope, and the *Mercury* lifted off the dewy ground into the cool morning air.

Clouds

Cirrus clouds mean changing weather, while light fluffy cumulus and stratocumulus clouds mean fair weather. Low grey stratus clouds often make fog and mist. Watch out for large swelling cumulus clouds – they could turn into cumulonimbus clouds and rain on you.

cirrus

cumulus

stratus

Fronts

If you see a line of clouds on one half of the sky and clear skies on the other side, this means a front is coming. Warm and cold fronts often bring brief rainshowers.

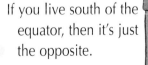

front

Wind direction

In the northern half of the world, winds coming from the north bring cold air and winds from the south bring warm air.

If you live south of the equator, then it's just the opposite.

Don't forget the Weatherbird's motto:

WATCH THE SKY!

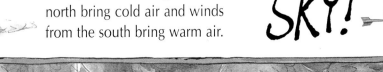

INDEX OF WEATHER WORDS

Numbers in darker type indicate main references